The cover shows the last moment of the Bear Flag Republic, Sonoma, July 9, 1846. The flag is being hauled down by Lieutenant Joseph W. Revere of the U.S. Navy, grandson of Paul Revere of 1775 fame.

Early
CALIFORNIA
& her flags

Gathered by Harry Knill
Drawn by Alan Archambault

Opposite: a flag of *E Clampus Vitus* was displayed July 4, 1856 by members from Greenhorn, Siskiyou County. It had a (green) horn on a green field. "The sign of this worthy fraternity was the raising of both hands to the ears, with thumbs against ears and fingers extended." Members were called by the "gegaw" or great horn.
Flag: R. Jones, *Saddlebags Siskiyou*

Back cover: Alvarado's flag, Santa Barbara, January 3, 1837

QUEEN CALIFIA

Ordoñez de Montalvo in his book *Las Sergas de Esplandin*, 1510, tells us, "On the right hand of the Indies there is an island called California, near paradise on earth, inhabited by black women who have no men among them, who live like Amazons. . . Their weapons are all made of gold. . . There are many griffins in California. . . when they are little, the women catch them and bring them up. They feed them with the men whom they take prisoners, and with boys who are born there."

OLD CALIFORNIA

In 1524 Cortés himself wrote the king of Spain about reports of the rich island of women. But not until 1532 was he able to send an expedition north to look for it, and the attempt failed when his enemy Guzman attacked. Cortés sent another expedition the next year under Grijalva and Becerra, whose crew revolted. Then, led by the pilot Jiménez, the mutineers found the lower California peninsula, where twenty of their men were killed. When news of the discovery reached Cortés, he led an expedition of 300 men and thirty-seven women to colonize the "Isle of Pearls" in 1535. In spite of the fortune that was spent on the colony, the land was too dry to support it. Cortés returned to Mexico, where his wife had been looking for him, and where he wanted to meet the new viceroy, Mendoza. Cortés's own standard, made in 1519, is shown, next page. For a long time it was in the chapel of the University of Mexico, where generations of students, praying for good grades, venerated it.

Flags on the opposite page: left, "probably the oldest flag in existence," said Preble, or at least one of the oldest, is of red damask. The pattern of twelve gold stars surrounding Mary Most Holy, *Revelations 12*, is a circular display of stars like that on some of our early Stars & Stripes, see *The Story of Our Flag*, Bellerophon Books. Right: black Imperial Eagle, golden crown and Golden Fleece and chain and many hues of much of European heraldry.

Cortes's flag, left opposite, is in the *Museo de Historia de Chapultepec*.

Cortés in Mexico with the Dove of Peace
on a pink flag; Codice Azcatitlán, Bib. Nat., Paris

HERNÁN CORTÉS IN OLD CALIFORNIA, 1535

JUAN RODRÍGUEZ CABRILLO, 1542

—came to the New World with Pánfilo de Nárvaez about 1510. He was a conquistador with Cortés and Alvarado and settled in Guatemala, where his gold mines financed shipbuilding. He built a fleet for Alvarado which set out on a voyage of discovery, but Alvarado died, crushed by a horse. Viceroy Mendoza took over and sent Rodríguez north "to discover the coast of the South Sea." He left Navidad, Colima, on June 27, 1542; on July 3 he was at the *Punta de California* and on September 28 he reached a "very good sheltered port" never before visited by Europeans. He named it San Miguel*; Vizcaíno later called it San Diego. He sailed on and soon reached some islands and met many Indians with fine canoes. Storms prevented him from rounding Point Conception, so he returned to San Miguel Island (his *La Posesión*) and then to Cicacut near Santa Barbara. There a woman was chief; he entertained her with bagpipes and dancing. He then went north and reached the Russian River, missing the great river he had heard of. On November 23, he was back at his island; on January 3, 1543, he died of a wound and was buried there.

AVE MARIA

GRATIA PLENA

Mendoza's flag: top and bottom: green, red, green, yellow stripes between; yellow sides

*Probably the name of his small *fragata*, shown here with his admiral's flag, as it was his launch. It was also the day before St. Michael's day. See H. Kelsey, *Juan Rodríguez Cabrillo*, 1986.

FRANCIS DRAKE & NEW ALBION, 1579

The "ancient national flag of England," a white banner with a red cross of Saint George.

There is no part of earth here to bee taken up, wherein there is not some especiall likelihood of gold or silver.

Huchee kecharoh (sit downe)!

This country our Generall named Albion (or *Nova Albion*) and that for two causes; that one in respect of the white bancks and cliffes, which lie toward the sea; the other, that it might have some affinity, even in name also, with our own country . . . sometime so called."

On June 17, 1579, Francis Drake found "a convenient and fit harborough" which was "continually visited with. . . nipping colds." His *Golden Hind,* having had a leak at sea, was emptied of the huge treasure cargo taken from the Spanish ship *Concepción,* 1,300 bars of gold and silver and 14 chests of jewels and gold, and grounded in order to trim her. The crew built a stone fort and walls, caulked the ship, and remained until July 23. The local Miwok called on the visitors; gifts were exchanged and their king, the Hyoh, "a man of goodly stature and comely personage" and his "tall and warlike" guard "made signe to our Generall to have him sit down. . . that he would take the Province and kingdom into his hand" and "honored him by the name Hyoh. . . wherefore, in the name and to the use of her most excellent majesty, he took the scepter, crowne, and dignity of the sayd country (Marin County) into his hand."

See R. F. Heizer, *Francis Drake and the California Indians,* 1947

Meet Don Gaspar de Zuñiga y Acevedo
THE YOUNG CONDE DE MONTEREY
9th Viceroy of New Spain, 1595 - 1603

Here Don Gaspar is shown at his home in the famous university town of Salamanca, where Cortés and Balboa had studied, as had the chronicler of Vizcaino's voyage, Fray Antonio de la Ascension. It was at Salamanca that Professor Victoria fiercely denounced the exploitation of the American natives.

Viceroy the Conde de Monterey thought it would be a good idea to chart the California coastline; perhaps a northwest passage might be found. Juan de Fuca was advertising one, from the Pacific Ocean to the Atlantic. Worrisome ships had been sighted on the Pacific coast; a rich Manila galleon, the *Santa Ana*, had been captured off Cabo San Lucas by the Englishman Cavendish, and another ship wrecked at Point Reyes. The viceroy wrote to the king, and a Royal Order was sent in 1599: map the coast without delay. Sebastian Vizcaino was appointed to lead it. He gave the viceroy's name to Monterey Bay.

Flags: left, arms of the University of Salamanca; right, Monterey's arms—see next page for colors.

MARIS PACIFICI

Quivera

Islas de los cedros

Cali=fornia.

Mar Ver-mejo.

Islas de los diamantes

Nova Hispania

THE ARMS OF THE NOBLE CONDE DE MONTEREY *

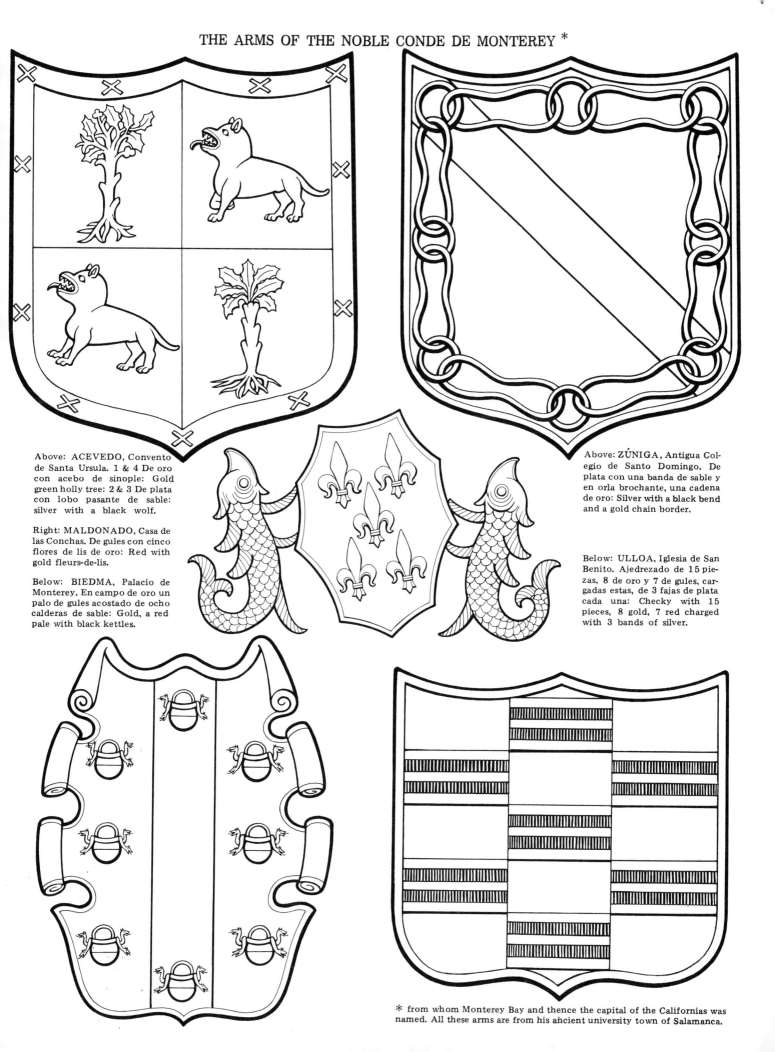

Above: ACEVEDO, Convento de Santa Ursula. 1 & 4 De oro con acebo de sinople: Gold green holly tree: 2 & 3 De plata con lobo pasante de sable: silver with a black wolf.

Right: MALDONADO, Casa de las Conchas. De gules con cinco flores de lis de oro: Red with gold fleurs-de-lis.

Below: BIEDMA, Palacio de Monterey. En campo de oro un palo de gules acostado de ocho calderas de sable: Gold, a red pale with black kettles.

Above: ZÚNIGA, Antigua Colegio de Santo Domingo. De plata con una banda de sable y en orla brochante, una cadena de oro: Silver with a black bend and a gold chain border.

Below: ULLOA, Iglesia de San Benito. Ajedrezado de 15 piezas, 8 de oro y 7 de gules, cargadas estas, de 3 fajas de plata cada una: Checky with 15 pieces, 8 gold, 7 red charged with 3 bands of silver.

* from whom Monterey Bay and thence the capital of the Californias was named. All these arms are from his ancient university town of Salamanca.

SEBASTIAN VIZCAÍNO
AT SAN DIEGO, NOVEMBER 15, 1602

Flags of Spain: right, Quarterly; 1 and 4 gules (red) a castle (Castile) or (gold): 2 and 3 argent (silver) a lion (León) rampant gules crowned or: en point (bottom) argent a pomegranate (Grenada) gules. Golden Fleece on a gold chain of flintstones and flames. Left: white field, red Burgundian raguled saltire (St. Andrew's cross) and border. Gold sun, moon.

On November 30, 1595, Sebastian Cermano's great Manila ship, *San Agustín*, was wrecked near Point Reyes. The survivors took the launch down the coast to New Spain, and after their return Viceroy Zúñiga became convinced that the coast of California should be properly charted—perhaps the fabled northwest passage might even be found. Sebastian Vizcaíno had a pearl-fishing company in Old California and knew something of the coasts. He was appointed general of the exploring expedition of the outer California coast, to chart it and all bays, rivers and islands. His fleet of three ships left Acapulco on May 5, 1602. His flagship, *San Diego*, reached the bay to which he gave that name on November 10. There a friendly native woman, "150 years old," met the explorers.

GENERAL VIZCAÍNO AND 180 JAPANESE VISITORS SEE UPPER CALIFORNIA

December 26, 1613

Vizcaíno's voyage to chart California was a success; two fine ports had been rediscovered: San Diego and Monterey. He praised Monterey in a letter to the king, and urged that it be settled. And as a reward for his survey, he was made general of the Manila ships, to steer them to Monterey. But then another port was wanted in the middle of the Pacific Ocean; he should go find the mythical *Islas Ricas de Oro* and *Plata*, thought to be near Japan, where the Portuguese had a trading monopoly. Tokugawa Iyeyasu, the shogun, was a good economist though, and wanted trade competition; he invited the Spanish there through his English shipbuilder, Will Adams. Soon free trade, more or less, was being discussed, and an embassy with twenty-three Japanese merchants went to Mexico in 1610. A Spanish ambassador was now needed—one who could also look for the Rich Islands of Gold and Silver and chart the Japanese coast. Who else, but the hero of the California coastline, General Vizcaíno? He and the twenty-three returning merchants sailed directly from Acapulco to Japan, and as soon as he was ashore there, he raised the royal banner of Spain. He even refused to doff his shoes at the Japanese court, perhaps because his crew was prevented from trading due to quibbles. Yet Iyeyasu asked the Spaniards to play the guitar for him, and amends were soon made. Vizcaíno charted the Japanese coast, and, as in California, named the bays anew.

Then Dutch and Englishmen, Spain's rivals, told the shogun Vizcaíno's charting was for a Spanish invasion of Japan. Iyeyasu became unfriendly, so Vizcaíno went looking for the Rich Islands. Not finding them, he left for home on a new Japanese ship, with 180 Japanese tourists. In two months, they reached California at Cape Mendocino and were at Acapulco January 22, 1614. Soon afterwards, Japan was closed to Spain.

See W. M. Mathes, *Vizcaíno*, 1968

After Kimura Kaheimon, 1632, Kiyomizu-dera, Kyoto

末吉

美しいカルフォーニアを訪れて下さい

HIS SACRED MAJESTY DON CARLOS THE THIRD

KING OF SPAIN AND THE INDIES, 1759 — 1788

under whom the occupation of our Alta California
took place by the direction of his able servants
the heroic Visitador Gálvez and the great
Viceroy Bucarelli y Ursua

THE ROYAL ARMS OF SPAIN AT THE TIME
OF THE CONQUEST OF ALTA CALIFORNIA

Quarterly: 1 and 4 gules (red) a castle (Castile) or (gold); 2 & 3 argent (silver) a lion (León) rampant gules, crowned or; en point (bottom) argent (silver) a pomegranate (Grenada) gules; surmounted by the arms of France azure (blue), three fleurs-de-lis or. Golden Fleece on a gold chain of flintstones and flames.

From *Real Ordenanza del Correo Maritimo,* 1777

JOSÉ GÁLVEZ
The Founder of Spanish Alta California,

Visitor-General of New Spain, 1769, "California's best friend," said Bancroft. In 1768, King Carlos III ordered San Diego and Monterey occupied to secure the coast from foreigners, particularly the Russians. José Gálvez had come to Mexico in 1765, with great powers from the king to reform the government. He had "practical good sense, business ability, untiring energy and disregard of all routine formalities that stood in his way," said Bancroft. Gálvez went to Old California and organized two land expeditions for New California, under Capts. Rivera and Pórtola, and two sea expeditions under Capts. Vila and Juan Pérez. The Franciscans, newly arrived in Old California to replace the expelled Jesuits, were to spread the faith above and Padre Serra told Gálvez that he himself would go on a land expedition.

Gálvez was "the foremost man in America," Bancroft noted, but still he helped pack for the voyage by sea. On January 9, 1769, at La Paz, Gálvez gave a parting address to those sailing on the small ship *San Carlos* for San Diego. They were going on a glorious mission, he said. Padre Serra blessed the pilgrims, the ship and crew, and the flag. The first expedition was off, with Lt. Fages and 25 Catalonian Volunteer soldiers on board. On July 1, 1769, Padre Serra limped into San Diego. Gálvez' four expeditions reunited there a year after he began his truly great preparations; 219 pilgrims had begun the journeys, and 126 remained alive. But Alta California now indeed belonged to Spain. Here are Gálvez' heraldic arms, with *banderas alcaladas*, representing his magnificence.

Gálvez after J.A. Gil, 1787

Vertical lines = red (gules)
Horizontal lines = blue (azur)
Dots = gold (or) Others their true colors (proper); *banderas alcaladas*: gules & or.

See: H. Priestley, *José de Gálvez*, 1916

NEC PIETATE FVIT·NEC BELLO MAJOR ET ARMIS · QVO JVSTIOR ALTER

AVE MARIA GRATIA PLENA

VICEROY Antonio Maria BUCARELI y Ursua, 1771-79 —who came to rule New Spain and wonderfully carried on Gálvez' work for New California. He constantly saw to it that urgently-needed supplies reached Monterey from the unwholesome port of San Blas. Padre Serra came down from Monterey to see him in Mexico City, and got nearly all he asked for his establishments. Capt. Anza wrote Bucareli for per-

mission to open a road from Sonora to Monterey, and it was granted with true encouragement. Bucareli sent Capts. Pérez, Bodega and Hecata to sea to explore the far northwestern coast. And he sent Señor Anza on his great second expedition overland, with settlers and cattle to establish a colony at San Francisco, which was founded Sept. 17, 1776.

VIVA LA FE !

VIVA EL REY !

Este puerto famoso de Monte-Rey . . . y planttar los estandartes de neustro Cathólico Monarca que Dios prospere.

PADRE JUNIPERO SERRA having arrived on the *San Antonio* at the FAMOUS PORT of MONTEREY, & Governor GASPAR DE PORTOLÁ, Captain of Dragoons, taking possession of the province in the name of KING CARLOS III OF SPAIN, JUNE 3, 1770

Flag colors are the same as Vizcaíno's but with gold fleurs de lis on blue (the Bourbon family now ruled) and gold and red pomegranate on white for Granada. Padre Serra: gray habit; *Soldados de Cuera* (ringing bells): white leather jackets, blue breeches, red or blue sleeves (uniform regulations for them were not yet established); black hats with red bands; Portolá: blue coat and breeches, red cuffs and vest, gold braid, etc.; Catalonia Volunteers: blue coats and breeches, yellow cuffs, vest, hat edging; brass buttons.

The king's red Burgundian saltire or Saint Andrew's cross of two logs, on Bourbon white

Build a fort to defend the port from the atrocities of the Russians who are about to invade us.

Without mistake we have found the port which Sebastian Vizcaíno drew in his log. The king of Spain has for centuries been owner and lord of these lands.

PADRES SOMERA AND CAMBON AND THE BANNER OF OUR LADY OF SORROWS, NEAR THE SITE OF SAN GABRIEL MISSION, EARLY SEPTEMBER, 1770

A great multitude of angry natives in war paint were there to attempt to stop the mission's founding. Fearing a battle, the fathers raised the beautiful image; at the sight of it, the Indians immediately threw down their bows and arrows in wonder.

Next: of all the early rulers of California, "there is no more original and attractive character than the bluff Catalan soldier Pedro Fages," wrote Bancroft. He arrived by sea at San Diego on May 1, 1769, marched to Monterey and San Francisco later that year and then made the trip again the next year, staying on in Monterey as commandant. When food ran out, he went bear hunting to feed his hungry troops. Padre Serra quarreled with Fages and went to see the Viceroy to have him recalled in 1774. But later, Serra felt sorry; "the honest Catalan" came back as governor in 1783 and remained until 1791. "He was industrious, energetic and brave, a skilful hunter and dashing horseman, fond of children, who were wont to crowd round him and rarely failed to find his pockets filled with sweets." There are other views, of course.

Gray habits

There was to be a fighting Indian woman leader in this neighborhood, Toypurnia, who fourteen years later led a furious revolt against the Spaniards.

"In this canyon are whole troops of bears. They plow the ground all up looking for roots for dinner. They are ferocious brutes and difficult to hunt. They attack with incredible speed and courage. A hunter can escape only on a very fast horse. . . We named the canyon *Cañada del Oso.*" It is just below San Luis Obispo. A little further on, "sixty hill Indians brought us a little bear cub. . . we named this the *Cañada del Osito.*"—Pedro Fages

FIRST LIEUTENANT DON PEDRO FAGES
(called *el Oso*)
AND HIS CATALONIA VOLUNTEER
LIGHT INFANTRYMEN IN THE
VALLEY OF THE BEARS,
SAN LUIS OBISPO,
May 12, 1772

LA COMPANIA FRANCA
I BTN.   II RGT.
DE LOS VOLUNTARIOS DE
CATALUÑA

Uniforms: blue coats and breeches, yellow collars, cuffs, coat turnbacks, hat bands, vests and buttons; white gaiters, stockings; golden epaulettes, buckles

Réné Chartrand tells us that flags of Spanish military units were generally not used below the regimental level, so this reconstruction more properly would have belonged at headquarters at Pachuca. Colors: white field, gold crown, red and gold stripes

SEÑOR DON JUAN BAUTISTA DE ANZA, LIEUTENANT COLONEL OF CAVALRY
& CAPTAIN OF THE ROYAL PRESIDIO OF TUBAC, SETTING OFF OVERLAND
FOR NEW CALIFORNIA WITH 234 PEOPLE, INCLUDING 30 FAMILIES, TO
SETTLE SAN FRANCISCO, OCTOBER 23, 1775, 11:00 A.M.

SAN FRANCISCO

EVERYBODY MOUNT.

Blue uniforms,
red facings,
collars, cuffs,
turnbacks;
brass buttons;
gold hat edging,
epaulettes;
black gaiters,
boots; white
hose; gray
friar's habit

Nolite timere pusillus grex.

Lt. J. J. Moraga

They then took with them:
"1 flag with royal coat of arms, price 12 pesos."

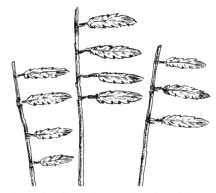

Anza had made the trip overland to Monterey and back the year before. His second expedition went under the patronage of Our Lady of Guadalupe, mother and patroness of the Indians and of America, promoter of spiritual conquests. Co-patrons were the Prince San Miguel, the Standard Bearer, shown holding the moon below, for the expedition had begun at San Miguel de Horcasitas, and also the "humble, excellent and singular saint," San Francisco, chosen by Padre Font and the commander, a brother of the Franciscan College of Querétaro. After travelling 165 days, the group arrived at Monterey on a wet March 10, 1776. On March 28 Anza chose the site for the new settlement and fort at San Francisco. "The port of San Francisco is a wonder of nature, and may be called the port of ports," said Font. The difficult trip had been a glorious success: "nobody even became (very) ill." It was due to these patrons and to Anza; "in the name of God and of the king our Lord I give thanks to our commander for the patience, prudence and good conduct which as chief he has shown in commanding this expedition," Font added.

PADRE FRANCISCO GARCÉS, THE INDOMITABLE EXPLORER OF THE SAN JOAQUIN VALLEY, 1776

He carried a banner with Mary Most High on one side, the Damned Man on the other, to better explain theology to the natives.

Padre Garcés travelled with Anza in 1775, as far as the Colorado River. There he worked with the Yuma Indians, and then he intended to go to the mouth of the river, visiting other tribes. By way of a detour he reached Mission San Gabriel in California and went on to explore the San Joaquin Valley. He had many adventures before he was killed by the Yumas in Chief Palma's uprising.

My principal goal was to make communication easier between Sonora and Monterey, which His Excellency the Viceroy wanted. But not succeeding in this because my Indian companions refused to go with me, I decided to go from San Gabriel to San Luis Obispo and then east to examine the tule marshes.

Gray habit; red-hot fire

Left: later Chumash or valley Indian banners described in the response of March 8, 1814 of Padres Tápis and Uria to the *Interrogatorio* of the Bishop of Sonora.

"In order to bring to happy success these important new establishments" Viceroy Mayorga ordered 70-year-old Captain Rivera to recruit *familias pobladoras* for the towns of New California, and troops to protect them. The settlers were given supplies, money and rations for three years. Rivera was to conclude recruiting in Guadalajara, whose arms are flown here, and he was supposed to receive necessary funds there from the *Real Caxa*. On August 25th, Rivera headed north from Sinaloa. In April, 1781, he and 42 soldiers with 30 families marched from Alamos, Sonora, towards New California.

CAPTAIN DON FERNANDO DE RIVERA Y MONCADA RECRUITING SETTLERS FOR THE PUEBLOS OF LOS ANGELES AND SAN JOSE & FOR THE ROYAL PRESIDIO OF SANTA BARBARA, 1780

On July 8, 1781, Rivera, a sergeant and six soldiers were killed by Chief Palma's furious Yumas on the Colorado River. The others had gone ahead and were safely at Mission San Gabriel, as were those who had gone by way of the sea and Old California. They founded Los Angeles on September 4 that year.

Por las Californias y el Pueblo de la Reina de Los Angeles

See: Instructions for Recruiting for California, Croix to Rivera, Provincias Internas, Tom. 122, Archivo General; flag: blue field, gold border, red crosses; gold lions, green-brown tree.
Uniforms: Capt. Rivera, blue coat & breeches; red collar, cuffs, waist coat. Drummer: reverse colors. Gold lace; brass buttons.

Don Pedro Fages came back to Monterey as governor in 1782; his highborn Catalan wife, Doña Eulalia de Callis, and their son Pedrito came up the Camino Real from Loreto the next year. She had been assured that California was not a barbarous place. But in California, she saw many poor, naked Indians; she felt sorry for them, and soon began giving them her own clothes, until she had hardly any. In 1784, a daughter was born to the Fages family. Then one day, Doña Eulalia tired of California and wanted to leave. But Don Pedro liked his job and refused to give it up. Doña Eulalia thereupon expelled Don Pedro from the house. Don Pedro had a beautiful Indian maid as a servant; this was probably Toypurnia, who had led a revolt at San Gabriel Mission and was brought north. Now Doña Eulalia became extremely angry. Don Pedro asked the padres at Carmel to help mend his marriage, while Doña Eulalia invoked the devil. She was to be sent to live in seclusion at the mission, but she refused to go and locked her door. Don Pedro broke the door open and carried her over to Carmel, then went south with Pedrito. Doña Eulalia grew still angrier. Don Pedro wrote from San Gabriel. He admitted her superior station and birth, but said he was unable to forget the outrage and shame she had heaped on him. Soon, happily, they were together again.

The ancient Royal Presidio of Santa Barbara, begun in 1782, is being rebuilt; you will surely enjoy visiting it.

White flag with arms of many hues from much of European heraldry; silver banner of the high-born doña's arms, with blue fleurs and dog. Catalonia Vol. uniform.

DOÑA GOBERNADORA, EL CAMINO REAL, 1783

NIKOLAI REZANOF
AND DOÑA CONCEPCIÓN ARGÜELLO
1806

Nikolai Petrovich Rezanof, Chamberlain and Ambassador from the Imperial Russian Court, represented the Russian American Company, which dealt in furs; he was the inspector of their establishments in Alaska. But the hungry Russians had little food, so Rezanof bought the Yankee ship *Juno* and sailed down to California for provisions. Don José Argüello was Commandant at San Francisco,* and Rezanof visited his house daily during his stay there. And there he met Don José's lovely daughter, Doña Concepción, fifteen years old. In time Rezanof asked for her hand and she consented, much to her parents' consternation. To marry, they needed the approval of both the pope and the tsar of Russia, so Rezanof began the long trip back to St. Petersburg. Alas, he became ill, fell from his horse, and died. Doña Concepción did not know this and refused all other suitors. Rezanof was energetic and clever and wrote of taking most of Alta California from Spain. Had he lived, a wonderful romance might have ended splendidly— and we might be Russians! The Russian Company, in any case, soon after established a post at Bodega Bay and then at Fort Ross.

*His *presidio* or fort guarding the bay was where the parade ground of the U.S. Army base now lies. It should be rebuilt!

Flag of the Russian American Company: white field, blue and red stripes below; brown eagle with yellow beaks and claws; gold crowns, scepter, orbs and chain; white scroll

Spain's American colonies were in full revolt, and free-booting sea captains were given letters of marque (licenses to steal) by the revolutionary chiefs, permitting them to take ships and ports flying the Spanish flag. On November 21, 1818, a ship of such insurgents opened fire on the fort above Monterey; the fire was returned by J.J. Vallejo from the water's edge. The ship was damaged and lowered her flag while the men escaped to the ship of the pirate chief, Bouchard, who then sailed up to the fort, demanded surrender, and was refused. The next day his devils landed and took both fort and town, which was burned before Bouchard went south to cause more havoc.

HYPOLITE BOUCHARD AT MONTEREY, 1818

Buenos Aires colors: sky blue outer stripes, white center stripe, golden May Sun; for more of this exciting adventure, see our *Dos Californios*

CALIFORNIA'S COLONIAL INDUSTRY

In their heyday, the missions' populations grew mightily, and hand grinding of grain for their many mouths became inadequate. Some of Spain's finest engineers, architects and master stone masons visited California, and remarkable industrial plants were built. A marvellous survivor is the huge milling complex at Mission Santa Ines, partially shown here; in 1810, 4,500 bushels of grain were raised and ground there, and by 1816 there were 768 souls to feed. This is how they did it.

With Bouchard came "el Yankee" José Chapman, who was captured and stayed and introduced the Californians to the marvels of American technology. The main product at Mission Santa Ines was sheep—12,000 of them. Imports from Mexico had nearly ceased because of Spain's troubles, and California had to produce her own supplies. For clothes, the looms in the mission shop were very busy, but the cloth was lumpy—it needed fulling (pounding). Governor Sola wanted a fulling mill built here, and Chapman knew how to do it. He made two plans, and Padre Uría sent one up to the governor for approval. We have that plan, and the building is extant near the grist mill opposite; the water from the overshot fulling mill went into the large reservoirs for the grist mill. Chapman was a thrifty New Hampshireman. After Bouchard's attack, it became clear that California needed more troops for protection. Captain Portilla came up with 100 men of the Mazatlan Cavalry Company (*Escuadron de Mazatlan*), a good outfit, and Captain Navarette brought up 100 rascals of the San Blas Infantry Company (Marines, *Veteranos de San Blas*), snatched unwillingly from the countryside of New Galicia. Such an army had never been seen before in California, declared Viceroy Apodaca. The soldiers were stationed up and down California; Padre Uría muttered about 5 *San Blaseños* stationed at Santa Ines.

Note: these splendid ancient mills are near the quaint Danish village of Solvang, which has a mermaid as the town emblem. While Mr. Hans Andersen was quite active during our period, his finny story hadn't yet emerged. But a water sprite was painted on the fulling building here, by an Indian hand long ago. Perhaps it was intended to propel the wheel when the water trickled. We take the liberty of imagining a kinship between these water folk. In any case, one of these days these great mills will be in operation again.

What say the Bells of San Blas...

They are a voice of the Past,
Of an age that is fading fast,
Of a power austere and grand,
When the flag of Spain unfurled
Its folds o'er this Western world,
And the Priest was lord of the land.
—Longfellow

LOS VOLUNTARIOS DE SAN BLAS

1820

Flag: white field, red cross of Borgona, gold crowns, banderas, blue cartouches; Uniform: blue jacket with red plastron (front), cuffs, collar; white pantaloons. Grayfriar. See J. Bueno, El Ejercito y la Armada, 1808, p. 148 (after Ordovas), p. 152. Also: Uría to Sola, Dec. 19, 1820, SB Mission Archiv Lib CMD 2019.

Governor Sola and Canon Fernández (see next page) watched while Ensign Estrada lowered the great flag for the last time. General Iturbide had set up a regency for King Ferdinando VII of Spain to come over and rule Mexico. When it was found that Iturbide was conspiring to overturn the Spanish monarchy and set himself up as emperor, fearless Nicolás Alviso attached some unflattering lines to a post nearby as the flag came down. Governor Sola smiled as he read them, but Canon Fernández tore them up.

Captain Navarette's San Blas Permanent Infantry Company

*Muera Iturbide
Con su gavilla
Muera su gente.
La California
Aunque indefense
Siempre valiente
Resistirá sus false-
dades
Con Brazo fuerte.*

Alviso

THE LAST MOMENT
OF THE GLORIOUS
FLAG OF SPAIN IN
ALTA CALIFORNIA
September 29, 1822

The old white flag of Spain was often mistaken for the white flag of France, so it was changed in 1785 to this flag of red-yellow-red, with a yellow castle on red, a red lion on white.

Sola was elected anyway to represent the Californians in the new Mexican congress. There he promoted a great company for California, the Asiatic-Mexican Company, with Monterey as a free port and headquarters. This would make California the center for all commerce with the orient, and for fishing, whaling and fur trading. The Company's flag was to be the Mexican flag with their initials, C.A.M.* on it. Sola saw how geographically and commercially important California would be.

* Companía Asiático-Mexicana, Vallejo I, 236

EL IMPERIO

MEXICANO

Flag: green, white, red

The ship *San Carlos* sailed into Monterey on September 26, 1822. Bells rang, soldiers ran to their posts, and Commandant Estudillo, with his flag book, spyglass and megaphone, went to hail the ship's captain, who then unfurled his flag at the mainmast. As soon as he saw the new Mexican flag, Estudillo opened up his flag book, but he could not find it. Governor Sola watched the ship from the church tower and was convinced that the men on board were from the newly independent Mexican nation. He knew that Viceroy O'Donoju's Spanish troops were too weak to have stopped the Mexican revolution for independence. A ship's launch came ashore and an important personage stepped out saying, "I am Agustín Fernández, canon with the Imperial Order of Nuestra Señora la Virgen de Guadalupe, and I come with important dispatches from Agustín I, Emperor of Mexico, whom may God preserve a thousand years (He preserved him for one), for the governor of this Province, Colonel of Militia Don Pablo Vicente de Sola." Governor Sola, knowing that none of New Spain remained in the hands of the Spanish, decided to obey the new government; had Sola known that the Emperor had already lost power while the *San Carlos* was sailing north, he surely would have refused to obey the Canon Fernández. An old Indian said, "At last has come to pass what we said would happen sooner or later: Mexico has returned again to the control of Mexicans." Several old soldiers of Spain were in tears when the glorious flag of Castile and León came down. Reveille *(toque de diana)* was sounded on the trumpet and the new national colors of the Three Guarantees of the Plans of Cordova and Iguala—Religion, Independence and Union—were unfurled. The Indians were delighted when they saw the triumphant eagle on the new flag, for that was their own sacred bird.

Viva la Independencia Mejicana !

Note: Another version of the Imperial flag may be seen in our *Rosie and the Bear Flag.*

Orden, Nov. 2, 1821, No. 254, que el pabellon nacional y banderas del ejercito deberan ser tricolores, adoptandose perpetuamente los colores verde, blanco y encarnado en fajas verticales, y dibujandose en la blanca una águila coronada.

Alvarado, Hist. Cal. I, 210
Bancroft, Hist. Cal. 2, 459

Viva el Emperador Agustín I.

JOSÉ MARÍA ECHEANDÍA, GOVERNOR OF ALTA CALIFORNIA, 1825 - 1831 AND 1833

Governor Echeandía liked San Diego (and a certain lady there), so it often became his capital. One day, he decided that the name of Alta California should be changed to Moctezuma, the name of the ancient Aztec king. A flag was proposed: a prehistoric chief was to be shown in an oval, coming to America across the Aleutian Islands,* with oak and olive trees as supporters. Governor Echeandía is best remembered as an ardent enemy of the missions, whose lands he wished to take back for the Indians. Remember that the missions then were somewhat like great medieval estates, which new republics should surely not have. When American settlers came, they felt the same way about the great California ranchos, which by then had been carved out of the old mission lands.

When Echeandía went to San Francisco, he climbed up Telegraph Hill and examined the great bay. "Mexico no sabe, no, lo que tiene," he sighed. "Mexico doesn't know what she has." Instead, Mexico began sending her worst criminals to this most remote place. This did not endear Mexico to the good Californians.

* One of the Russian arguments for claiming land on the west coast of North America was that its inhabitants had originally come over from Russian territory.

One fiesta day in 1827, a bear and bull fight took place in the plaza of San Diego, in front of the Presidio church (you can see its foundations on the hill above Old Town). Sr. Bull soon tired of Sr. Bear, and as the church was built right into the hill, the former climbed onto the roof to fight the tiles.

Gov. Echeandía: green coat with bright red breast; gilt epaulettes, embroidery & buttons; flag: white field & blue oval & scroll (the colors of Montezuma); gold scroll & leaf work; brown trees, green leaves, blue sky, green ocean, etc.

Once, when there were many
wars, a woman became great
captain or princess, Luhui, of
the four channel islands. Then
there was peace.

See Fernando Librado,
Kitsepawit, to John
Harrington, *The Eye
of the Flute*, 1977

Native ceremonies were often mixed with Christian festivals at the missions. Here Martina—a fine dancer, wearing
the *tsuh* crown and holding *plumeros*, dances the Seaweed Dance while holding onto the banner of Captain Luis
Francisco of Saticoy. The boys carry images representing wind, fire and water. *Siliyik* red feathered banners and
feather poles, each representing a rancheria, were raised with flute playing as Chief Luis's pet bear cub entered.

The Little Red Pennants
VICTORIA'S END, Dec. 5, 1831
THE BATTLE OF CAHUENGA

Lt. Col. Don Manuel Victoria came up as military chief in 1830 and lasted a year. He succeeded Echeandía, who had passed a Decree of Secularization of the missions, to take their lands away from them. This was fostered by J.M. Padres and the Californians. Conservative Victoria, like President Bustamante, didn't approve of this; he annulled the decree and refused to call the Territorial Assembly. When Victoria, without authority, kicked people out of California, they became vindicitive. So, on November 29, 1831, the Californians at San Diego plotted a revolt. The leaders were J.A. Carrillo and Abel Sterns, exiles, and J. Bandini and Pío Pico. They wrote up a grand *pronunciamiento* of their griefs, and took over the San Diego presidio. Ex-governor Echeandía was persuaded to lead the revolt to oust Victoria, and to replace him. Capt. Portilla of the Mazateco Squadron had 60 men under his command, but 30 were up in Santa Barbara, so when Sr. Victoria passed by there he took those men under Capt. Pacheco to accompany him. There were then 30 Mazatecos on each side. Capt. Portilla led his men from San Diego and some citizens from there up to Los Angeles, where about 200 more joined the army. Victoria arrived

from Monterey at San Fernando on December 4, with the men from the north. The next day the two forces moved towards each other, and met at Cahuenga, near the present intersection of Highways 101 and 405. Capt. Portilla occupied some hills. Then Victoria arrived, his men in a formation five deep. When within shouting distance, Victoria ordered Portilla to abandon his rascally revolutionaries and join him. Portilla ordered Victoria to halt; Victoria returned an insult. Pacheco ordered the advance and met Don José Ávila, at whom he slashed with his sabre. Ávila parried with a lance; Pacheco's horse rushed by. Ávila shot him after he passed and killed him instantly. Ávila still had a second shot for Victoria, who was wearing a red flannel shirt. Ávila's horse jumped; his lance went into Victoria, who fell, while at the same time Ávila received a bullet in his hip. Victoria approached with his sword to finish Ávila off, but Ávila grasped Victoria's foot, and as he fell Ávila reached for his dagger, but it was lost. When Carrillo and Portilla saw the dead, they realized that revolution was not such an easy thing and left the wounded Victoria on the battlefield. Victoria was carried off to San Gabriel Mission and treated by Joseph Chapman, the American of   pages back. Echeandía arrived there and Victoria transferred the government to him. The Territorial Assembly was then called to meet at Los Angeles, and Victoria was sent back to Mexico.

The Mexican eagle in California, from the flag of the
Monterey Customs House and now on display there.

In 1834, Vice President Gómez-Farías sent a colonizing party of 239 people up from Mexico City, to take over the rich lands of the missions of Alta California. *Señores* Hijar and Padres were the Colonizing Directors, and they were to take over the California government—they thought. They were also Directors of the Cosmopolitan Mercantile Company, the foundation of which was their colony, to be installed on mission lands, and the civil and military governorships, one for each gent. After Victoria was expelled (he had earlier kicked Padres out of California for troubling the padres), General Figueroa came to Monterey to rule. "The Cosmopolites wish to enrich themselves on the ruin of more than 20,000 Indians, who are the legitimate owners of the mission property," he said. And the good Californians did not want the mission lands snatched away by anybody—but themselves. A revolution with some colonists broke out in Los Angeles. Others of the party went to Sonoma, from where they intended to found a town near Santa Rosa. It had been reported that Padres threatened, with any change in government in Mexico, that he'd make California independent or annex it to the United States. Change did come, for President Santa Anna returned to rule Mexico, and he decided

LA COMPAÑIA COSMOPOLITANA

Protectora de la Industria en la ALTA CALIFORNIA

La Compañia Cosmopolitana was the realization of La Compañia Asiatico-Mexicana (para el mas pronto fomento de las Californias), which had a flag proposed and described, but never became a company. Although we can not at present put our finger on a source for the flag here, we are more than certain that one existed.

to stop this fun in California. He sent a messenger, Rafael Amador, off on July 25, 1834, to ride furiously from Mexico City to Monterey to tell Governor Figueroa not to deliver the territory to Hijar. Amador arrived on September 11 after just 48 days—an immortal ride—and gave the happy message to governor Figueroa. The governor then ordered Ensign Vallejo to arrest the colonists at Sonoma, and Hijar and Padres were soon expelled from California. But over 200 of the colonists seemed to like it here even without riches, and remained.

Mexican colors; uniform: blue coat with red collar, cuffs and plastron (front); blue pantaloons; gilt epaulettes and buttons. Red tassels.

Let the mission lands be distributed to the Indians, for they are the sole owners.

—General Figueroa

See: Figueroa, *Manifiesto a la República Mejicana . . . sobre su conducta y la de los Señores D. Jose Maria de Jihar, y D. Jose Maria Padres, como Directores de Colonización en 1834 y 1835*, Monterey, **1835**, or C. Hutchinson's edition, **1978**. Also, his *Frontier Settlement in Mexican California*, **1969**.

In 1830 Lieutenant Colonel Manuel Victoria came up to rule. He tried to keep the mission lands for the missions, so he was defeated by the unappreciative Californians at a battle near Los Angeles in 1831. In 1833 General José Figueroa came up to govern. He soon died, and probably for that reason he was the only governor from Mexico applauded by the Californians. In 1836 came Colonel Mariano Chico, and he too was chased away, after four months. Lieutenant Nicolás Gutierrez was then left in charge, and he, also, vexed the Californians; "he decided to dissolve the Territorial Deputation with bullets or swords." The deputies met secretly at San Juan Bautista. Young Juan B. Alvarado knew the rights of free men, and "determined to banish Gutierrez from California" A revolutionary plan was put into action. José Castro assembled armed revolutionists at San José and the ranchos, and Alvarado went to Sonoma to enlist M.G. Vallejo as Commandant General. Vallejo had over one hundred troops and said he could provide one hundred more, including Chief Solano and his Suisun warriors. American *rifleros* and sailors from ships at Monterey joined, too. The little army of now over three hundred met at the Pajaro River and prepared to attack Monterey.

THE FREE
AND
INDEPENDENT
STATE OF
CALIFORNIA
November 6, 1836

"The flag is to be six stripes & one Star, they say," T. Larkin to Abel Stearns, Nov. 9, 1836, Bancroft Library. The Alvarado forces attacked the fort with "A Mexican flag having a black eagle in the white part," said F.D. Atherton. "On entering the place their flag was hoisted." "It was reported. . . that a flag had been prepared for the *new Republic*," said Alfred Robinson; "It was the Texian—the Lone Star. They never made use of it, however, but continued to administer their government under the Mexican banner." *Life in California*, p. 176. He said elsewhere, though, "A new Star appeared." Letters. "A new flag to contain a single star was being made ready," said Petit-Thouars, *Voyage*. Colors: red star on six white stripes. This flag is in the Southwest Museum, Los Angeles.

First the fort on the hill was captured, and the only cannon ball available was sent down around the ears of Gutierrez, who then surrendered and was exiled to the bottom of Baja California. A new flag, shown here, was said to have been used by Alvarado's Free and Independent State of Alta California.

Flag colors unknown.
Uniform colors: dark blue
jacket, green collar and
cuffs, red plastron
(front) and cuff bars,
white piping; dark
blue pantaloons,
red stripe. Brass
buttons, epaulettes
and chin strap.
Black shako. See:
Nieto, *El Soldado
Mexicano,* 1958

History comes from lots of sources, and so does our knowledge of California's early flags. Before the camera, most people drew somewhat. But in California, paper to draw on was scarce. At the College of Guadalupe at Santa Ines, founded in 1844 by Bishop García Diego, there was a musty old library for the scholars to peruse— and use it one did, to sketch in the pages. While we hope he wasn't caught, for his fate may have been grim, we can thank him for showing us uniforms and a banner from the time of Governor Micheltorena. The "B" no doubt stood for a troop of Barbareños, the balance of power between Montereyanos and Angelinos, or rather between *norteños* and *sureños.*

There was concern in Mexico that California would be taken by another nation, so General Micheltorena was sent up to save her—with an army of convicts, which horrified the Californians. Commodore Jones of the U.S. Pacific Squadron thought that war was probably breaking out with Mexico because of Texas and that the British Squadron was about to take California, violating the Monroe Doctrine. He decided to beat them to it. He got to Monterey first; there Alvarado, the California governor, was said to prefer surrendering to the Americans rather than to Micheltorena. Monterey was captured and the Stars and Stripes were raised on October 20, 1842. Then Jones learned that there was no war or incident to allow him to do this, so he gave Monterey back. When Jones went to apologize to Micheltorena in Los Angeles, he noted how elegantly the officers there were dressed. Micheltorena wanted Jones to provide uniforms, which might make his convicts look respectable as well. He also asked for musical instruments, for he knew that California was a land of uprisings, which were generally won by the musicians. Jones's mistake surely meant that the U.S. had an eye on California. Many of the Californians at the time regretted his giving back their country.

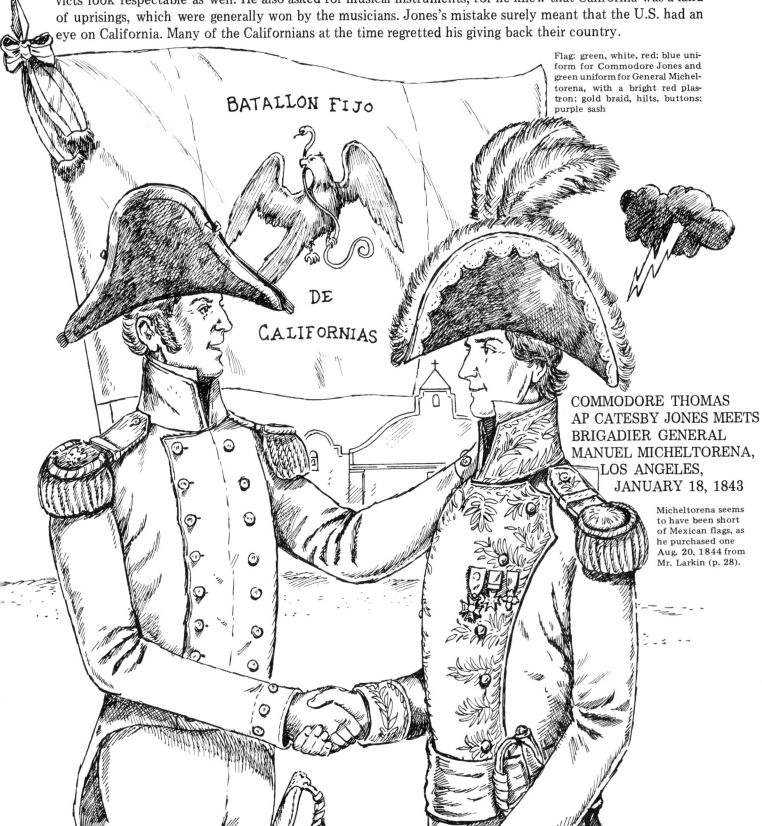

Flag: green, white, red; blue uniform for Commodore Jones and green uniform for General Micheltorena, with a bright red plastron; gold braid, hilts, buttons; purple sash

BATALLON FIJO DE CALIFORNIAS

COMMODORE THOMAS AP CATESBY JONES MEETS BRIGADIER GENERAL MANUEL MICHELTORENA, LOS ANGELES, JANUARY 18, 1843

Micheltorena seems to have been short of Mexican flags, as he purchased one Aug. 20, 1844 from Mr. Larkin (p. 28).

THE HUDSON'S BAY COMPANY

Fur trappers of the HBC first entered the Sacramento Valley around 1828. By 1832, they had large companies of trappers up and down California. Sir James Douglas, Chief Factor of the Company, was there in 1841 and noted that California was "in many respects unrivalled by any other part of the globe." He came both for business and "with objects of a political nature in view." The few British inhabitants of California thought it a fine prospect for a British colony. If Britain should obtain it (by way of repayment of Mexican debt, for instance), that would stay the expansion of her rival, Brother Jonathan (or Uncle Sam). Douglas wrote that the HBC ought to buy or build premises at the Yerba Buena; Alvarado soon permitted this. William Rae, a jolly bonvivant, was sent from Fort Vancouver to establish the post. He bought an old building from Jacob Leese, who moved to Sonoma. Mrs. Rae came down to join her husband. Poor Mr. Rae: he had fallen in love with a lovely Californian lady, and business turned bad. The romance was discovered by his angry wife, and Rae, who had supported the Californians in their revolt against Micheltorena, feared ruination. Poor Rae shot himself. Soon afterwards, in 1845, the Hudson's Bay Company post was abandoned.

British Union of red crosses of Saints George and Patrick, white cross of Saint Andrew against blue; red field, white letters, purple hearts.

HUDSON'S BAY CO.

Rae's End, January 19, 1845

OREGON & CALIFORNIA
Farnham & Hastings

While negotiating with Spain over Florida in the time of President Monroe, John Quincy Adams had insisted that the territory north of California, west of the Rockies, also be ceded to the United States. The U.S. thus gained the old Spanish title to what is now Oregon, Washington, Idaho and some of Montana and Wyoming. But in 1827 the U.S. and Great Britain agreed that Oregon would be jointly occupied, for both countries claimed the territory. Besides the Spanish title, the U.S. claim was based on Gray's discovery of the Columbia River in 1792, Lewis and Clark's expedition in 1805/6, Astor's fur-trading settlement in 1811, and the presence there of American missionaries and settlers, who thought the border with Canada should be far up at 54° 40'—or fight. But the British claimed it on the basis of their own discoveries. To make it American indeed, more settlers were wanted. Thomas Jefferson Farnham went overland from Illinois to Oregon in 1839. The intention of his party of nineteen 'Oregon Dragoons' was to win Oregon for the American flag and to resist the British fur-trade monopoly. When he got there, he urged the Willamette settlers to petition Congress to take them under U.S. protection. He then took a ship to California by way of Hawaii and arrived at Monterey just as Isaac Graham and other American and British citizens were being arrested and sent in chains to Mexico. Farnham helped them. He also decided California should become American. His 1844 book, *Travels in the Californias,* was widely read in the east and inspired great interest in California. In 1842, Lansford W. Hastings joined Dr. White's party of 160 people leaving Missouri for Oregon—the first large expedition over the Oregon trail. Soon young Hastings was captain of the group. From Oregon Hastings went south with a small party to Sutter's fort. There, he decided that he liked California, too. He wanted to get enough immigrants into California so that he (and Sutter too, he said) could "revolutionize the country."

Eliza Farnham made the flag shown here for her husband's 1839 expedition; we have taken it from a description in his *Travels in the Great Western Prairies. . . and in the Oregon Territory,* 1843. Mrs. Farnham came to California in 1850; seeing many men and very few women, she went east and recruited ladies to come west and bring some civilization with them, as that was quite lacking during early American times in California.

and fight the Spaniards. He began writing his famous *Emigrant's Guide,* where he describes the lovely climate and fertile fields. He went east to lecture and recruit and so missed the Bear Flag function and the chance to be president of a new republic. But he did much to bring settlers when their presence was crucial for the events unfolding in California.

THREE WHO PUT CALIFORNIA IN THE U.S.A.

Colonel Thomas Hart Benton, Senator from Missouri, Jessie Benton Frémont &"The Pathfinder," John C. Frémont

ROCKY MOUNTAINS 1841

—the officer in command has to appear. . . as the representative of the government. '43

Flag: lilac field, gold letters; Frémont covered their new baby Elizabeth with this on Nov. 13, 1842. Mrs. Frémont gave the flag to the Southwest Museum. See *Masterkey,* v. 26, 1952.

Col. Benton long argued for the westward expansion of the U.S. to the Pacific Ocean. Lt. Frémont was with the U.S. Topographical Engineers, surveying in that direction; when back in Washington, he met the senator's daughter, Jessie, and married her when she was 17, causing the senator's ire. The other side of this flag is among the most famous of American flags. The lieutenant raised it on Frémont's Peak, in what is now Wyoming, 13,730 feet high, on August 15, 1842. It has 13 stripes with a white canton containing an eagle with a peace pipe and arrows. Frémont gave it to Jessie, who backed it with the side shown here, cut from her silk wedding dress, and embroidered the words on it.

It is probable that next year I shall be sent to continue these Explorations to the Pacific. —Nov. 16, 1842

We all know how Frémont set off the Bear Flag function, about his capture of California, about how he became governor of California and U.S. Senator, and how he ran for president in 1856. Jessie was a mighty powerhouse, too, and one reason why California became a free state in the Union. For during the Constitutional Convention in Monterey in 1849, as she said, "My pretty rooms were the headquarters of the anti-slavery party . . . our decision was made on the side of free labor."

THE BEAR FLAG, SONOMA, JUNE 14, 1846

In 1846, John C. Frémont was annoying the Californians with his band of sixty "Topographical Engineers." Senator Benton, his father-in-law, was the most powerful man in Washington and had a long involvement with westward expansion. We do not know preciesly what he or President Polk told Frémont, but a secret message from Polk was

Brownish red star, bear, stripe on white field

CALIFORNIA REPUBLIC.

"We are bound to defend it or be shot." *H. L. Ford*

carried to him in the mountains by Lieutenant Gillespie of the Marines. This message has never been seen or told, but we assume it said: war is breaking out with Mexico. Start a pro-American revolution in California and frustrate Britain or France from grabbing it before our forces arrive, which will be soon. Now there had been many California revolutions and pro-American Californians before Frémont arrived, but his insults insured that there would be no more friendly uprisings. So Frémont met with the rough American mountain men around Sutter's Fort; we do not know what he told them, either. But the next thing, Sonoma was captured by thirty-two "uncouth and ferocious" men and the "Bear Flag Republic" was born. The Bear Flag flew twenty-five days and was replaced by the Stars and Stripes, July 9, 1846.*

*"I hauled down the bear flag," Revere, Sacto *Enterprise*, Oct. 10, 1875. In 1849 he called the Bear "rampant;" it wasn't. Our cover suggests why he did.

General Vallejo, his brother Salvador and Prudon, his secretary, were made prisoners by the Bear Flag men and taken to Frémont's camp on the American River and then to New Helvetia, Sutter's Fort. A while later, some new recruits, travelling from Sonoma to Sutter's, "made a Bear Flag of our shirts to hoist when Frémont should arrive (from Sonoma, too). . . Frémont was much pleased to see the flag we had made. . . When I got to the fort the 'lone star' was flying. The colors was made of the old Mexican flag."* Back in Sonoma, Doña Francisca Vallejo ordered the men to take down their flag. "If you want to have peace on the frontier, order down that rag and run up the American flag," she demanded. Lieutenant Revere arrived to do just that late on July 9th, and at 10:00 the next morning he took down the Bear and unfurled Old Glory "among the thundrous cheers of all the Californians there." He proceeded to Sacramento and when he arrived Old Glory, unfurled high on a staff, was marched past the fort to Frémont's camp three miles away. It was raised at the fort at sunrise July 11, to booming cannon. "Mein Gott, boys, you will prake all mine windows!" said Sutter.

SUTTER'S FORT
JULY 10, 1846

The Vallejos

scalp

CALIFORNIA REPUBLIC.

Kit Carson, Frémont's scout

Sutter

Frémont

Red Lone Star
* Flag source: *Reminiscences of Old Times* by "Bear Flag" (J. Wm. Russell), *Napa County Reporter*, Feb. 2 - June 22, 1861, reprinted in *The Hist. Soc. So. Cal. Quarterly*, Mar., 1951

THE STARS AND STRIPES ARE UNFURLED OVER CALIFORNIA

"It was on the 7th of July, 1846, a day forever **memorable** in the annals of California, that **Commodore Sloat**. . . sent **Captian Mervine** ashore at the head of 250 sailors and marines and, without firing a shot, took possession of the fort and plaza of Monterey amid the hurrahs of the people, who were pleased to see waving in the old capital a flag which Thomas O. Larkin (the American consul) had taught them to regard as a symbol of the most unalloyed liberty."

General Vallejo

It is not only our duty to take California but to preserve it afterwards as a part of the United States at all hazards.

Com. Sloat

Opening a school as the first act of your administration must be placed to your credit and honor as a thing of a primary importance to the welfare of California. Larkin

U.S.S.   SAVANNAH

Consul Larkin and Commodore Sloat

Downcast was Gasquet the French consul; "the French warship arrived at Monterey when the American flag waved. Otherwise it is probable that the French flag would have been raised."

—*Alvarado*

In 1829, Captain James Arthur of Plymouth, Mass., raised the first Stars and Stripes in California that we know of at his warehouse for hides on the beach at San Diego. He made the flag from shirts and flew it to attract company from the few ships which occasionally sailed by. Seventeen years later in the midst of war: Commodore Sloat and his ship *Savannah* arrived at Monterey July 1, 1846, joining the U.S. war ships already there. On the 4th of July the fleet was dressed with the hundreds of flags aboard, and sailors saluted from the yard arms of the ships. Monterey's inhabitants expected that the Americans would march ashore and take California that day, but Sloat hesitated. Consul Larkin had told him that the Californians might themselves separate from Mexico and ask for U.S. protection. But there was also a strong party of Californians who instead favored a British California, and the British Admiral Seymour, with his huge ship-of-war the *Collingwood*, was on the way to Monterey. Finally Sloat said, "I have determined to hoist the flag of the United States at this place," and at 10:00 A.M. Tuesday, July 7, Old Glory was raised at the Customs House amidst cheers. An American flag had been made for the Fourth of July at the Caymus Ranch, Napa Valley, by Virginia and Patty Yount for a big public dinner. Later that year in San Diego, the Bandini sisters made a gorgeous U.S. flag for the American soldiers and sailors who were preparing to march north to recapture Los Angeles. The young ladies were serenaded and thanked by Commodore Stockton, who had taken Commodore Sloat's place.

THE FIRST STARS & STRIPES
MADE IN CALIFORNIA

Isadora

Acadia

Commodore Stockton

Yount's *Chronicles,*
ed. C. Camp, 1966

Bancroft III, 135,
and V, 356

CALIFORNIA & HAWAII
Commodore John Paty of the Royal Sandwich Navy, 1846

Flag: British Union as before (given Kamehameha by Vancouver); 8 stripes representing the major islands, alternating white, red, blue starting at the top. See V. Houstan, *The Hawaiian Flag*. Note: the Hawaiian flag first came to California on the Waverly, 1826, under Capt. Wm. G. Dana of Boston. He married Josefa Carrillo and settled at Nipomo. For Paty, see Cal. Hist. Soc. Quarterly 14, 1935.

Americans increasingly foresaw an American Hawaii. Sam Brannan who stopped there in 1846, had plotted a private adventure to capture the Islands

In the days of the ranchos, as afterwards, there was much coming and going between California and the Sandwich Islands, mainly in Yankee ships. Californians sent their children to missionary schools in Honolulu, and the Hawaiians rode around their islands on horses from California. American whalers, naval and merchant ships of all kinds rested and traded there while sailing to and fro over the Pacific Ocean on their way to California. Nobody sailed between the two places in those days more than Capt. Paty. He was even born on Sandwich Street in Plymouth, Mass., in 1807, a descendent of Mayflower settlers there. He went to sea at nine and first arrived at Honolulu in 1834 and in California the same year. King Kamehameha III in 1846 gave him a commission as his "naval supervisor," with a gallant uniform and responsibility to see to the welfare of the many Hawaiians in California, mostly excellent sailors; by 1865, Capt. Paty had made 100 voyages between Hawaii and here.

SAM BRANNAN AND THE MORMONS, 1846

The Mormons had intended to emigrate to California, and Sam Brannan, an extremely enterprising Yankee, led 238 of them on the ship *Brooklyn* to the then-promised land. They left New York on February 4, 1846—on a ship flying a flag saying OREGON to confuse their opponents—and arrived at Yerba Buena ("what an odd, uncouth town") on July 31. There they found the U.S. flag waving, something they had not expected when they left. They had brought their own 'Standard of the Prophet' to raise, but now they were too late to take California themselves, even though they arrived with uniforms and muskets to do so. Still, these industrious people arrived at a most propitious moment.

"I shall hoist a flag with Oregon on it." *S. Brannan,* Jan. 26, 1846. "Then it came out on trial in civil suits . . . that the Brooklyn company was designated by the authorities of the Church at Nauvoo to unfurl the standard of the Prophet on the shores of the Pacific." *Sacto. Daily Union,* Sept. 11, 1866. The Prophet's standard was white with *Peace* across it in red letters. F. Brodie, *Jos. Smith,* 1971, 148. See also Phelps, *Fore and Aft,* 296.

Sister, see yon evening star,
Shining o'er the hills afar!
Shines it not for you and me,
Over the California sea?

Rejoice! rejoice!
The wilderness
shall bloom !

OREGON

FRÉMONT'S CALIFORNIA BATTALION

Companies B and G, 1846

Republic of California

By July 9th, Monterey, Yerba Buena and Sonoma* had been taken by the U.S. Navy under Commodore Sloat. But Los Angeles, the capital, and all of the south still flew the flag of Mexico. Frémont enlisted the Bear Flag men ("160 ex-Osos") in his new California Battalion under Commodore Stockton, who soon took command of the Pacific Squadron. Frémont's men went by sea to San Diego and raised the Stars and Stripes there. Stockton landed at San Pedro. His sailors met Frémont, and together they took Los Angeles on August 13 1846. But it was soon lost.

* See cover.

Blue flag with red, white and blue flags and arms thereon; white guidon with red star and stripe, brown bear

Sources: *Wide West*, Oct., 1856; the battalion flag was donated to the Society of Cal. Pioneers in 1855. The San Francisco fire of 1906 destroyed both that and the Bear Flag guidon, which had been donated to the Society by Revere (*Sacramento Enterprise*, October 10, 1875).

There were a number of stalwart black volunteers in Captain "Hell Roaring" Thompson's San José Pueblo Company G.

A BRAVE HERO AT NATIVIDAD FIGHT, NOVEMBER 16, 1846

Captain Burroughs was taking horses from Sacramento to Monterey for Frémont's march south when a horseman with a Mexican flag was seen near the Salinas river. Scouts were sent to reconnoiter; suddenly, they were surrounded by Californians under Joaquin de la Torre. C. Burrass's Indian sharpshooters came up; the Californian standard bearer was mortally wounded. Instantly, Mariano Soberanes leaped from his horse, wounded the enemy who had taken the flag, recovered the flag, took his friend in his arms, put him back in the saddle, and, passing through enemy fire, took him to safety. C. Burrass ordered a charge and dashed ahead, through the thick of the fight. Juan Boronda rode up abreast, flourishing a flag in one hand, and with the other sent a bullet through C. Burrass, who had just pointed a rifle at Boronda. The other Americans were lucky to escape, but the Californians' old muskets were more dangerous to the users than to the enemy.

Hurrah for Jackson!

LOS VOLUNTARIOS DEFENSORES DE LA PATRIA

Y DEPARTAMENTO DE CALIFORNIAS

Mariano Soberanes

Flag: green-white-red: brown eagle; uniforms: green jackets, blue pantaloons with black stripes; silver buttons, red sashes; black hats

Sources: Alvarado, *Historia de Cal.*, 5, Ch. 43
E. Kemble, *California Star*, Aug. 21, 1847;
Sacramento *Daily Union*, Nov. 23, 1869,
Dec. 2, 1871, in *A Kemble Reader*, 1963

Juan Cantua

General Kearny took possession of New Mexico on August 18, 1846, and annexed it to the U.S. as part of Texas. On Sept. 26 he left there with 300 First Dragoons to take California. Along the way he met Kit Carson, who told him that Stockton and Frémont had already taken California, so Kearny sent 200 men back. It was still a long, long journey to California, and conditions could change before the dragoons got there. On the cold, rainy night of December 5 at the Indian village of San Pasqual, near San Diego, Andres

Pico and about 100 California cavalry were searching for Captain Gillespie of the U.S. Marines and his thirty-nine men, who had gone out to lead Kearny to San Diego (Pico thought they had merely gone to catch cattle to feed Stockton's sailor-army there). Lieutenant Hammond led a party of six dragoons to scout out this enemy camp. "Clang, bang," all of a sudden went his big dragoon sword. "Bark, bark," roared back a village dog. The Californians woke up and were on their fine horses "in a twinkling," then waited.

Blue flag, gold stars, brown American eagle with white head and yellow beak and claws, red scrolls with gold letters and volutes, red and white stripes in shield, blue above, green leaves, brown arrows with gold arrowheads; guidon: red on top with white letters; white below with red letters and numbers; uniforms: dark blue jackets and caps, light blue trousers, yellow stripes, chevrons, trim; gilt swords; white belting

Very early the next morning, Captain Johnson gave the order "Trot," but it was mistaken for "Charge!" "Oh, heavens, I did not mean that," said the general. About forty dragoons were now charging down on the Californians at top speed. Kit Carson had said that the Californians would not fight if the dragoons merely yelled, and the dragoons wanted the Californians' horses, for their own were worn out after so many months and miles of deserts and mountains. Carson, the great hero that he was, was wrong! Californian lances and pistols and riatas met the Americans. Captain Johnson, bravely leading the charge, fell dead. Soon more dragoons appeared. The Californians retired.

Captain Moore led another charge. Suddenly Pico's lances wheeled around and charged the Americans. There was a terrible fight, hand to hand and lances and riatas outreached swords. Thirty-five Americans were killed and wounded; twenty-one died out of just forty-five who had seen the enemy. No Californians were killed.

U.S.
C Comp.
1st
DRAGOONS

*Find the enemy, Carson,
and we'll fight them tonight.*
—Kearny at the Gila River

*We might have a little
kick-up with the good
people of California.*
—Dr. Griffin

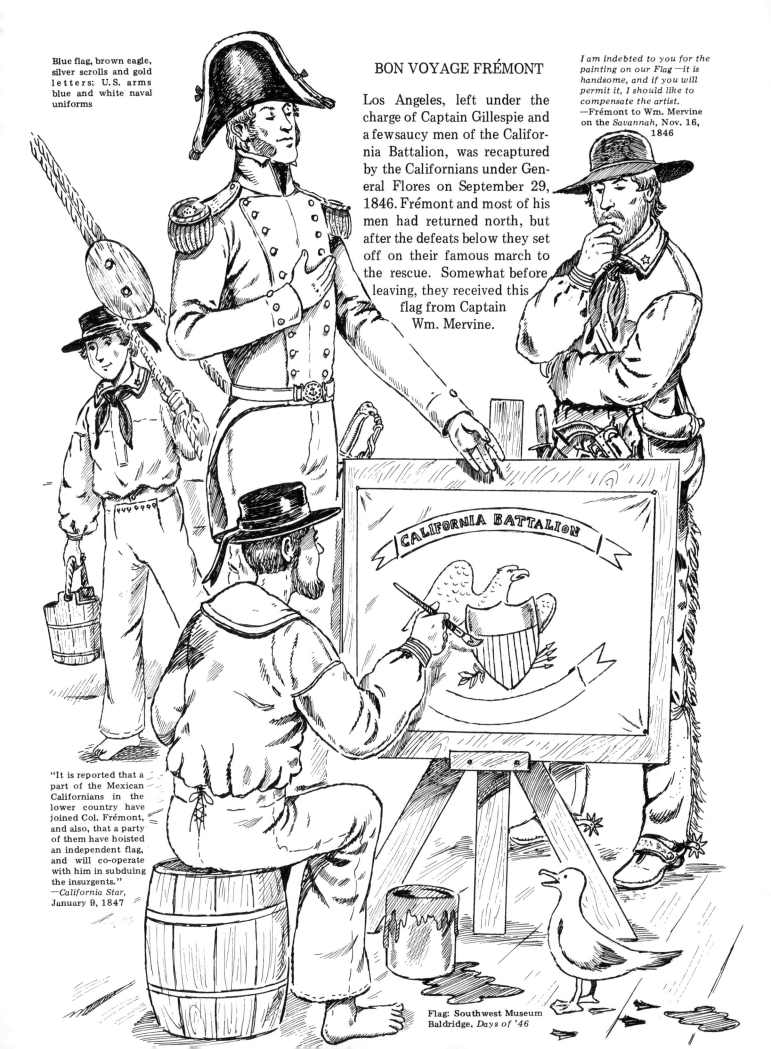

Blue flag, brown eagle, silver scrolls and gold letters; U.S. arms blue and white naval uniforms

BON VOYAGE FRÉMONT

Los Angeles, left under the charge of Captain Gillespie and a few saucy men of the California Battalion, was recaptured by the Californians under General Flores on September 29, 1846. Frémont and most of his men had returned north, but after the defeats below they set off on their famous march to the rescue. Somewhat before leaving, they received this flag from Captain Wm. Mervine.

I am indebted to you for the painting on our Flag —it is handsome, and if you will permit it, I should like to compensate the artist.
—Frémont to Wm. Mervine on the *Savannah*, Nov. 16, 1846

"It is reported that a part of the Mexican Californians in the lower country have joined Col. Frémont, and also, that a party of them have hoisted an independent flag, and will co-operate with him in subduing the insurgents."
—*California Star*, January 9, 1847

CALIFORNIA BATTALION

Flag: Southwest Museum
Baldridge, *Days of '46*

THE NEW YORK VOLUNTEERS, 1847

"Success to California, likewise to Oregon; and the rooster that crows there must be Uncle Sam!" So sang the Broadway boys when recruited to go with Colonel Stevenson and his Regiment of New York Volunteers to California. They sailed off on Sept. 26, 1846, and arrived at Yerba Buena in March and April, 1847. The City of New York had presented them with a fine full set of regimental colors—the state flag and guide colors. The New Yorkers were assigned to garrison duty up and down the California coast. On July 4, at the Ciudad de Los Angeles, they gave a magnificent ball, to which came all the elite of the city. The regiment's flags decorated the ball room.

It was a grand success, for they had brought with them a choice regimental band of twenty-four instruments, which won the Californians.

EXCELSIOR

Sources: F. Clark, *Stevenson's Regt.*, 1882
J. Lynch, *With Stevenson*, 1896; J. Hollingsworth, *Journal*, Cal. Hist. Soc. Quar., Jan., 1923

Blue flag, light blue sky on shield, white ribbon, brown eagle and mountains, yellow sun and crown; blue uniforms, red cuffs, sash, collar fronts, stripes; gold epaulettes, buttons

THE BATTLE OF SANTA CLARA, January 2, 1847

"Just as soon as Frémont marched south the natives in the north who were opposed to the Americans immediately took up arms," wrote Mrs. Hecox. Alcalde Midshipman Bartlett and five men of Yerba Buena had gone on Dec. 8, 1846, to "purchase" supplies around rancho San Mateo and were captured by Francisco Sánchez. Soon Sánchez had a force of 100 men, who had taken up arms "to protect themselves from depre-

YERBA BUENA COMPANY SEMPER PARATUS OF VOLUNTEERS

Flag: "Our watchword is inscribed upon our banner, and we trust that you will find us semper paratus." Captain Smith, Feb. 6, 1847, Bancroft, V, 383
See: M. Hecox, Overland Monthly, 1892

dations" of the conquerors; the latter took this to be a new revolt. Capt. Weber and his mounted San Jose Pueblo Company of 33 riflemen—sailors, whalers and landsmen, rode up to Yerba Buena and there joined Capt. Ward Marsten with his company of 24 U.S. Marines, 10 sailors with a cannon and 12 mounted Yerba Buenamen under Capt. Smith—101 men altogether. Down the peninsula they marched and spied the enemy on Jan. 2 near Santa Clara.

Marsten fired his cannon and Sánchez replied with musketry, charged and wounded two Americans, and then he retired to the Santa Cruz mountains. The fight took place in plain view of the mission. Over 100 Americans under Capt. Aram were camped at the mission, but most of the men had gone south with Frémont. Several women said they could shoulder a musket, and Mary Bennett "waltzed back and forth in front of the mission yelling orders to the men at the top of her voice. Growing more excited she ran forward and grabbing up a large bone lying in the yard, rushed up to a man who had refused to fight, saying he had no gun. Stopping squarely in front of the startled fellow she thrust the bone into his hands and

shouted, 'take that, you puppy, and go out there ... or I'll use it on you,'" said Margaret Hecox. That evening Sánchez sent a messenger with a truce proposal that they would submit if the Americans would guarantee protection of their property.

"This ended the war in upper California. Both parties shook hands and a friendly feeling existed on both sides." M. Hecox

MORMON BATALION 1847

MRS. WIMMER TESTS MARSHALL'S GOLD

James Marshall and Captain Sutter were partners in building a sawmill, and several boys of the Mormon Battalion* were working on it. Jennie Wimmer was doing the cooking; when Marshall discovered gold in the millrace on January 24, he gave her the first nugget he found. She tested it the next day by boiling it in lye. "From that time the fever set in and gold was on the brain."

Coloma,
January 25, 1848

"But for the Mormon volunteers ... there might have been no discovery of gold in California for decades."
—Horace Bell

*The Mormon Battalion, mustered into the U.S. Army, made a very famous long march of over 2,000 miles to San Diego and arrived just after California had been taken. The men did tremendous work there, and wherever they went in California, especially after their discharge. Battalion boys were most active in the early gold discoveries. Then they went to Utah, many by way of Sutter's fort and mill. One of the boys took this flag back with him. The flag is in the Pioneer Village, Farmington, Utah; it was presented by the grandson of the boy who made it and carried it across the plains. The five stars and five stripes represent the five companies of the battalion. (From a letter of Peter Freed, Curator.)

White flag, red and white stripes, red and blue letters and numbers, yellow edging and front of 4; yellow and blue stars

THE '49ERS OVERLAND

The Gold Discovery was wonderful news for "the restless rovers of all nations, particularly the enterprising and impudent Yankees." Overland companies were formed in every corner of the country for protection and safety on the road to California; some wore uniforms and some had flags. This Ohio company had thirty men, ten light wagons and forty young mules. Companies often agreed to mine for gold together on a one-for-all plan, but as some were lazy and others ambitious, this never worked out. All of the companies disbanded soon after arrival, if not before. No fewer than 6,000 wagons set out in '49 from St. Joseph, Mo., for California. Some emigrants even walked there. Mrs. Hurd, here, was restored to health by walking. "Women seem to undergo the hardships of this journey with uncommon philosophy," said Decker, the driver here.

Flag source: P. Decker's Diary, 1849, Soc. Cal. Pioneers

COLUMBUS CALIFORNIA INDUSTRIAL ASSOCIATION 18 49

CALIFORNY OR BUST

CARSON CUT OFF 40 MILES (NO WATER)

"It was a strange feature in their journey, that the few women and grown-up girls were comparatively robust and healthy, while the men were worn and ailing, notwithstanding that the greater portion of the hard labour, since their sufferings commenced, even to the hewing of wood and driving of teams, had been performed by the females. The spirits of the latter, too, were high and elastic, and often seemed to counteract the lethargic despondency of the men." W. Kelly, *A Stroll Through the Diggings of California*, 1852

Yankees had been sailing around Cape Horn to California since 1796; they knew the way there well. Late in 1848 ships loaded with gold seekers began leaving eastern ports in a rush for El Dorado. Passage was costly, so mainly gentleman adventurers went by sea, though an overland passage could cost even more. Ships sailing around Cape Horn or through the Straits of Magellan averaged 180 days. Some sailed to Chagres and from there travelled across the Isthmus to Panama, then took ship for San Francisco. On February 28, 1849, the Pacific Mail Steamship *California* arrived in San Francisco, beginning a faster era. A huge portion of the young men of New England sailed to California. They formed companies for trading and mining, and most companies owned their own ships. In New Bedford and Nantucket even whaling ships were converted for California expeditions; it was feared that nobody would be left home to vote.

Here is a gentleman of the Cambridge with the Mount Washington and Rox-gold fringe by Dr. Pierce of Brookline. *Sweden* arrived in San Francisco 154

Company; when about to sail from Boston on March 2, 1849 bury Companies, he was presented this banner of white silk and The inscription means "Ever Higher." Their ship days later, where they are shown encamped.

Then ho! Boys, ho!
Who to California go,
For the mountains cold
Are covered with gold,
Along the banks of the
Sacramento.

EXCELSIOR

Flag source: O. Howe, *Argonauts of '49*, 1923, p. 62

Continued in *THE STORY OF CALIFORNIA & HER FLAGS 1849 to now.* You'll adore it.